Lord Jim

Joseph Conrad

Academic Industries, Inc.
West Haven, Connecticut 06516

ISBN 0-88301-754-7

Published by
Academic Industries, Inc.
The Academic Building
Saw Mill Road
West Haven, Connecticut 06516

Printed in the United States of America

about the author

Joseph Conrad was born in Poland in 1875, the son of parents who loved their country and fought against its takeover by Russia. Although young Joseph loved Poland, he did not plan to spend his life there. At the age of twenty he left for England, which became his adopted country—at least as far as his writing career was concerned.

During his twenties Conrad spent a great deal of time at sea, and many people believe he was involved in smuggling. But these years were well spent in the sense that what he learned about the sea and the strange ports and the jungles could be used later in his novels. And in spite of the fact that some of his early activities may not have been legal, he somehow learned to have a great respect for English law.

In *Lord Jim*, Conrad shows his readers a man who cannot live without being able to do good. This is why Jim, after being a coward early in the book, spends the rest of his life trying to undo his "evil" deed. Other books by Conrad which involve the same theme of inner struggle are *Heart of Darkness*, *The Secret Sharer*, and *Nostromo*. Joseph Conrad died in 1924, one of England's best-known novelists.

LORD JIM

Joseph Conrad

Marlow

Jewel

Lord Jim

Doramin

Stein

He was an inch or two under six feet, strongly built, and always dressed in white. To the men on the docks, he was "Jim."

Of course he had a last name, but he never told anyone what it was. And, since he moved often from port to port in the Far East, no one really cared about his family history. Only the Malays, who met him when he had left the ports of the white men, ever gave him another name. They called him "Tuan Jim" or "Lord Jim."

During the years he worked in the seaports of the Far East, he made his living as a ship's chandler's clerk.

Be quick, Jim! There's a ship coming in!

In his job, Jim had to race to any ship coming into port. He had to get there before any other clerk did.

Welcome to Rangoon! My boss sends his greetings.

Here is his card. You'll not find a better ship's chandler anywhere!

Then he would take the captain to the great shop filled with everything used on board ship.

You're a smart fellow to know exactly what I need!

Jim's the best clerk I've ever had.

Jim seemed to know everything about ships without ever having been a sailor.

He was, in fact, a sailor away from the sea. With him he carried a dark secret, and sooner or later someone would always learn of it.

Say, haven't I seen you before?

He knows me! It's time to leave this place!

I'm sorry, sir, but I'm quitting.

Now, Jim, if you want a raise in pay, you know I'll give it to you.

Good clerks were hard to find, and Jim was always well liked. But he didn't stay anywhere too long.

It's just time for me to move on, sir. If you knew my past, you would *want* me to leave.

We've all got something to hide. You're a good man today, and that's enough for me.

But Jim kept moving east. As the years passed, he was known in Bombay, Calcutta, Rangoon, Penang, and Batavia.

Jim had grown up in an English village where his father was the parson.

The church on the hill had stood there for many years, and the trees around it had been there even longer. Jim's family had lived in the village for as long as he could remember.

Jim was one of five sons.

We give thanks for this food.

When Jim became interested in the sea, he was sent to a training ship for officers in the merchant marine.

Remember son, a single bad act can destroy a man's life. Never do anything you know is wrong.

On the training ship, Jim learned the special arithmetic that sailors need.

He learned how to walk across the topgallant yards.

He did well in everything. Soon he led the other men whenever they rowed the small boat.

Follow Jim, lads. He's the one to watch!

From his place on one of the high masts, he often looked down on the world. How much better he felt than those others below! Surely he would have wonderful adventures at sea and do great things.

But down on deck he often drifted off into daydreams.

He daydreamed about saving people from sinking ships and capturing pirates. He was always the hero in his own fairy tale.

The men were on their way.

Too late, lad. Next time you must be quicker!

Soon the cutter returned with a boatload of survivors.

Jim was angry. He felt he had been cheated out of a chance to show how brave he could be.

But soon he was lost again in dreams of adventure.

After two years of training, he went to sea. But life at sea had little adventure. Mostly it was just hard work.

Yet he could not go back. Besides, he did his job well, and while still very young he was made first mate of a fine ship.

In all this time he had never been tested—never had a chance to prove he was brave.

Coil that line! Do it right!

16

Once, how-ever, he saw the real anger of the sea.

The ship battled a storm that lasted for nearly a week. But on the first day, Jim was hurt by a falling beam.

I don't know how we'll make it through this one!

After the storm, the days were beautiful. But when they reached an eastern port, Jim had to go to a hospital.

He was left behind when the ship sailed again.

As soon as Jim could walk without a cane, he was down on the docks.

Any ships in port that need a first mate?

Aye, the *Patna* there does.

PATNA

She's a steamer—as old as the hills and eaten up with rust. She's worse than an old water tank.

But Jim signed on as first mate.

Welcome aboard the *Patna*.

She was owned by a Chinaman, chartered by an Arab, and the captain was a fat old German.

18

The Arab had chartered the Patna to take eight hundred pilgrims, young and old, rich and poor, to their holy city.

Look at those people!

When they were aboard, they sailed out toward the Red Sea.

The Arab sang for them the prayer for travelers by sea, and the trip began.

One night Jim stood watch alone.

Below him the eight hundred pilgrims slept peacefully. They trusted completely in the captain and crew.

As usual, Jim drifted off into his daydreams. The moon hung in the sky like a tiny golden pin.

What a peaceful moment!

We've hit something! Quick, Jim, go check the forward hold.

But be quiet! Don't upset anyone. We haven't enough lifeboats for everyone.

The people on deck were still sleeping soundly.

It's flooded! I'd better check the bulkhead!

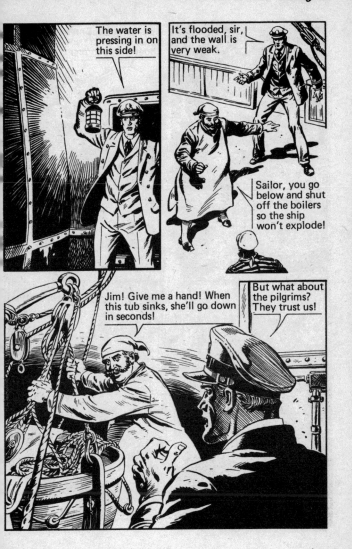

Take a last look at Jim, the hero, boys!

Come on! Don't be a fool! This storm will sink the ship for sure!

But Jim couldn't move.

Hey! The third engineer is missing!

Hey, George! Jump, George, we're down here!

But the third engineer had suffered a heart attack.

There are 800 living people here, and all they care about is saving a dead man!

Just then the storm hit.

Jump! Jump!

The ship began to roll.

I can't stay here! I don't want to die!

And so Jim landed in the lifeboat.

I feel terrible! I wish I were dead!

The storm passed. Morning came, but there was no sign of the Patna.

She sank for sure in that storm.

Say! You're not the third engineer!

Soon they were picked up by another ship.

We did everything we could. She sank so fast we barely saved our own lives.

But when they got to port, the captain was called before the harbor master.

You're a liar and a coward! The *Patna* was found without a crew on board. A French boat towed her home safely.

Outside, the captain spoke to Jim.

There will be a trial. If you're such a hero, stick around. I won't be back!

The other two sailors got drunk and were sent to the hospital. Only Jim was at the trial.

Without thinking of their duty, this man and three others rowed away in a moment of danger. Behind them they left the people and property they were trusted with!

The trial went on all day.

Today we have heard the facts of this case. Tomorrow you will hear what we have decided.

As Jim left the courtroom, he heard someone speak.

Look at that dog!

What did you call me?

I didn't say a thing about you. I was speaking of this poor fellow.

Forgive me. It's been a hard day.

Well then, why don't you dine with me at the Malabar House? My name is Marlow.

Ever since I was a child, I dreamed of the brave deeds I would do. But when the moment came, I wasn't ready.

Let me lend you some money. Leave town tonight. You have suffered enough for your mistake.

What a chance I missed!

Thank you, but I have to see this through. Then I must find a way to make up for what I've done!

The next day, Jim went back to court.

We find you guilty. Your sea papers will be taken away. You can't get a job at sea without them.

Too bad you ran away, sailor!

Now he'll drown himself in an ocean of drink!

Jim walked around the city, not knowing what to do. That afternoon Marlow found him down by the docks.

I'm no better than a tramp now!

If you'll come to my hotel this evening, I may be able to help you.

I have written a letter for you to bring to a friend of mine. He owns a rice mill in another city. I've asked him to give you a job.

Thank you. I will try to live up to your trust.

And so Jim began his life away from the sea.

Well now, my friend Marlow says you're down on your luck and need some help. Someone helped me once, and I'll pass it on to you.

For several months things went well.

That Jim's a good worker.

Yes, I've grown to like him a lot.

Jim, you're welcome to your own room here in my house. You've begun to seem like a son to me.

Thank you, sir. You've been very kind.

But one day the second mate of the Patna *showed up and was given a job at the mill.*

Now Jim, my boy, I see you're well liked around here. I won't say anything about the *Patna* if you'll take good care of me.

Jim left that very day. Back he went to the seaport.

I hear you need a clerk.

One day he saw Marlow again.

You were a fool to leave your old job. My friend would have given you everything. Why didn't you trust him?

I thought it would break his heart. I just couldn't tell him about my past.

It was just one unlucky chance in a hundred that the mate showed up.

But one chance will follow you wherever you go!

And so it was that Jim began to wander from port to port hiding from his past.

Marlow traveled a great deal. He saw Jim several times.

Perhaps you should try to find work in America. I could send you there.

No, I see that I've been running for years.

But I've also been searching—searching for a way to feel like a good man again.

Yes, you have! I've tried my best to help you, Jim, but I know someone who may be able to help you where I've failed.

That evening Marlow visited his old friend Stein.

Stein was a rich old trader who had seen many adventures. He knew what it was like to fail at something.

Welcome, Marlow.

Friend Stein, I have a story I must tell you.

Marlow told Stein about Jim.

Yes, I can understand this story very easily. Your young friend must find a way to prove himself. I know just the place for him.

Is there a cure for him?

I'm afraid there is no cure. But he may be able to help himself!

Look at this butterfly. It is so fragile, yet so strong. This is the way nature works.

The butterfly finds something to land on and he sits there, very still.

But man will never sit still. And, when he thinks he is a devil, he always wants to be a saint!

He loves to daydream about being good—and brave. But only in his dreams will he ever be perfect!

You live in a dream, too! But unlike poor Jim, you've caught your dream—these beautiful butterflies!

Well, yes. You may be right.

But do you know how many I've let escape? And how many I've lost?

And some would have been very fine. Everyone has at least one or two like that, and that is the trouble.

But enough! Send your friend to me. Tomorrow I will do something for him!

The next morning Marlow sent Jim to Stein.

Young man, I think we can help each other.

I have a trading post in a faraway place called Patusan. The man whose place you will take is named Cornelius. I will give you a letter for him. I would like the man and his daughter to remain in their house for I am sure they have no place to go.

It is a dangerous post. There are three people you will have to deal with.

One is a robber named Rajah Allang who rules the Malay people. The second is a thief named Sherif Ali who rules the country tribes. There is one good man—Doramin, the chief of the Bugis.

You will find no peace there unless you can make it yourself. It may cost you your life.

I'd like to go, sir. This is the chance I've been praying for!

That day Jim sailed on one of Stein's ships. After many weeks they came to a fishing village.

Patusan is forty miles up that river. We'll drop you here.

Very well, then, take this ring to Doramin. He gave it to me when I saved his life. Perhaps it will help you.

At first no one wanted to help Jim.

It is many years since any white man comes here. Rajah Allang will kill you.

All I ask is a boat ride to Patusan. I'll watch out for my own life.

The village chief finally sent some men to take Jim up the river.

Jim drifted off to sleep in the boat. Suddenly he awoke. They had reached shore, but there was trouble.

Men with spears forced Jim to go to Rajah Allang's fort.

You have Stein's ring. You are welcome here.

And then Jim fainted.

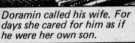

Doramin called his wife. For days she cared for him as if he were her own son.

Soon the fever will pass.

As he got better, Jim became friends with Doramin's son, Dain Waris.

It is many years since I have had a friend like you.

And I have never had one like you!

When Jim was well again, he wished to go to Cornelius.

Do not go. Here you are safe. If you cross the river, the Rajah or Sherif Ali will kill you!

I will never forget how kind you were to me, but I must go.

And so he crossed the river.

This letter says I'm fired.

You may stay in your house. But I must see the account books.

Books? Er, well, my wife lost them. And she is dead.

Just then a lovely girl drew near.

Come here, daughter!

You are not my father!

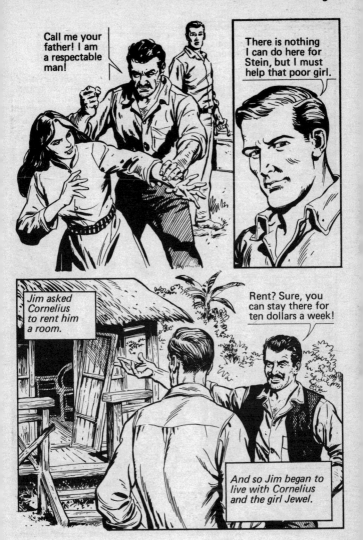

Call me your father! I am a respectable man!

There is nothing I can do here for Stein, but I must help that poor girl.

Jim asked Cornelius to rent him a room.

Rent? Sure, you can stay there for ten dollars a week!

And so Jim began to live with Cornelius and the girl Jewel.

Some nights later, Jewel awoke Jim in the middle of the night.

Take this gun and run! Sherif Ali's men have come to kill you.

I'll take the gun, but I won't run away. Will you help me?

Jewel led Jim to an old storeroom where Ali's men were waiting.

Throw down your knives!

Jim had to shoot one man, but the others gave up.

Don't worry, I won't kill you. I want you to tell Sherif Ali that I will visit him soon.

Jim led them to the river and made them jump in.

Good night. Watch out for the alligators on your way home!

Then he turned to Jewel.

I stayed to help you, but you helped me instead.

Cornelius is filled with hate. He would have led those men to you. I could not let them hurt you.

Come with me tonight. You must never return to Cornelius.

Oh, Jim! My heart is open to you.

But I am afraid you will leave like the others—like my father.

Do not worry. In all the world there is no one who could take me from you!

They went to Doramin's village. The next morning Jim spoke with Doramin himself.

Sherif Ali is like a hawk who circles over the chickens. He kills us from above, and we can do nothing to stop him.

If you trust me, together we shall put an end to this!

Doramin and Dain Waris agreed to Jim's plan. That night they secretly moved two old cannons up the hill across from Sherif Ali's fort.

I will go with Dain Waris and your men. We will use the sunrise for our signal. When you have fired the cannons, we will attack.

When the sun rose, Doramin's cannon balls ripped through the walls of Ali's fort. Then Jim and Dain Waris led an attack.

Sherif Ali and his men were taken by surprise. Many were killed. Sherif Ali escaped, but he was never seen again in that country.

Jim was a great hero.

There is no one in the world braver than Tuan Jim!

And no one smarter!

Rajah Allang gave up his guns and promised to live in peace. Soon Jim built a new trading post and made many friends. One was Tamb' Itam.

Tuan, please let me be your servant.

You are welcome here always. You may join us and build a house for your family.

Jim showed the people of the village many things.

Tuan Jim, you have taken away our fear. And more, you have shown us how to be free from want.

And you have given me much more than I can ever tell.

The years passed happily for Jim and Jewel.

Each day is filled with joy now.

I want this to last for-ever!

Then one day Marlow came to Patusan.

I bring good news. Stein is so happy with what you've done that he wants to make it all yours!

You both have given me so much!

Marlow stayed for a month. Jim took him everywhere and showed him everything.

This is where we defeated Sherif Ali.

You have proven yourself to everyone. I am proud to have helped you!

But there were other moments too. One day Cornelius caught Marlow alone.

Jim is your friend. Make him give me some money. I will take care of Jewel when he is gone.

Gone? Jim loves Jewel and Patusan. He will never leave!

What! You mean he will stay forever?

When Stein's ship returned, Marlow prepared to leave. Marlow was happy for Jim.

I don't expect that you'll leave here, or that I'll ever come back.

Then this is goodbye.

Forever.

Forever.

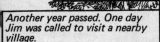

Another year passed. One day Jim was called to visit a nearby village.

I'll be back in a few days. Jewel will take over while I'm gone.

The next day some pirates rowed up the river.

See! I told you we'd find a fat little village!

But Jewel and Dain Waris were ready.

They had given the people guns. Together they drove the pirates up a small hill where they were trapped.

Then Jewel and Dain Waris met with Doramin.

We have sent for Jim. He will know what to do.

That is good. But Dain Waris should take some men down the river in case there are more pirates.

And so it was. When Jim returned, he called a truce and spoke to Brown, the pirate leader.

What made you come here?

We were hungry! What made *you* come here?

Jim shuddered. Brown had touched his only weak spot—his fear of his past.

Look here, I'm like a rat in a trap. But even a trapped rat can bite.

Not if you don't go near the trap until the rat is dead.

Come, now. We meant no harm. We only wanted some food. Your people attacked us. Give us an open fight or a clear road back to sea. We'll starve if we stay here.

That's just what you deserve.

Brown tried again.

And what do you deserve for *your* past?

All right, you win. But I must speak first with Doramin.

These are bad men. Surely we should kill them.

I say let them go. If any harm comes of it, I will answer for it with my own life.

Then Jim went to his house.

Are these men very bad?

Men act that way sometimes without being much worse than others.

Then he called Tamb' Itam.

Take this to Dain Waris so he will know that you speak for me. Tell him not to worry or fight. Brown and the pirates will leave in peace.

Jim sent word to Brown to leave the next morning. When morning came, Cornelius went to see the pirates.

I can show you how to get even with these people.

Come along, then. I see you're a friend.

Cornelius led them to Dain Waris' camp. The pirates began shooting.

Dain Waris and many others were killed. The pirates ran away, never to be seen in Patusan again.

Only Cornelius had been left behind. Tamb' Itam saw him standing nearby.

Cornelius, you are a dead man!

Then Tamb' Itam paddled up the river to bring the sad news to Jim.

Tuan, they have killed Dain Waris!

Quick! Run to the village and gather some men. We must chase them and kill them.

My people will blame you for the death of Dain Waris. I may be killed for serving you.

Suddenly Jim knew that he had failed again to care for those who had trusted him.

Jim walked through the village to Doramin.

I promised you my life if anything went wrong. Well, here I am.

The silver ring was brought to Doramin with the body of his son, Dain Waris. As Doramin rose, the ring fell from his lap.

Jim watched the ring roll toward him as Doramin fired. Jim had finally paid the price for his past.

THE END

COMPLETE LIST OF POCKET CLASSICS AVAILABLE

CLASSICS

C 1 Black Beauty
C 2 The Call of the Wild
C 3 Dr. Jekyll and Mr. Hyde
C 4 Dracula
C 5 Frankenstein
C 6 Huckleberry Finn
C 7 Moby Dick
C 8 The Red Badge of Courage
C 9 The Time Machine
C10 Tom Sawyer
C11 Treasure Island
C12 20,000 Leagues Under the Sea
C13 The Great Adventures of Sherlock Holmes
C14 Gulliver's Travels
C15 The Hunchback of Notre Dame
C16 The Invisible Man
C17 Journey to the Center of the Earth
C18 Kidnapped
C19 The Mysterious Island
C20 The Scarlet Letter
C21 The Story of My Life
C22 A Tale of Two Cities
C23 The Three Musketeers
C24 The War of the Worlds
C25 Around the World in Eighty Days
C26 Captains Courageous
C27 A Connecticut Yankee in King Arthur's Court
C28 The Hound of the Baskervilles
C29 The House of the Seven Gables
C30 Jane Eyre
C31 The Last of the Mohicans
C32 The Best of O. Henry
C33 The Best of Poe
C34 Two Years Before the Mast
C35 White Fang
C36 Wuthering Heights
C37 Ben Hur
C38 A Christmas Carol
C39 The Food of the Gods
C40 Ivanhoe
C41 The Man in the Iron Mask
C42 The Prince and the Pauper
C43 The Prisoner of Zenda
C44 The Return of the Native
C45 Robinson Crusoe
C46 The Scarlet Pimpernel

COMPLETE LIST OF POCKET CLASSICS AVAILABLE
(cont'd)

C47 The Sea Wolf
C48 The Swiss Family Robinson
C49 Billy Budd
C50 Crime and Punishment
C51 Don Quixote
C52 Great Expectations
C53 Heidi
C54 The Illiad
C55 Lord Jim
C56 The Mutiny on Board H.M.S. Bounty
C57 The Odyssey
C58 Oliver Twist
C59 Pride and Prejudice
C60 The Turn of the Screw

SHAKESPEARE

S 1 As You Like It
S 2 Hamlet
S 3 Julius Caesar
S 4 King Lear
S 5 Macbeth
S 6 The Merchant of Venice
S 7 A Midsummer Night's Dream
S 8 Othello
S 9 Romeo and Juliet
S10 The Taming of the Shrew
S11 The Tempest
S12 Twelfth Night